Jig and Mag

by Bobby Lynn Maslen
pictures by John R. Maslen

Scholastic Inc.
New York • Toronto • London • Auckland • Sydney • Mexico City • New Delhi • Hong Kong • Buenos Aires

Beginning sounds for Book 7:

J j – 🫙 jar

W w – ⌚ watch

ISBN 0-545-02720-9

6 5 4 3 2 1   7 8 9 10 11/0

Printed in China
This edition first printing, September 2007

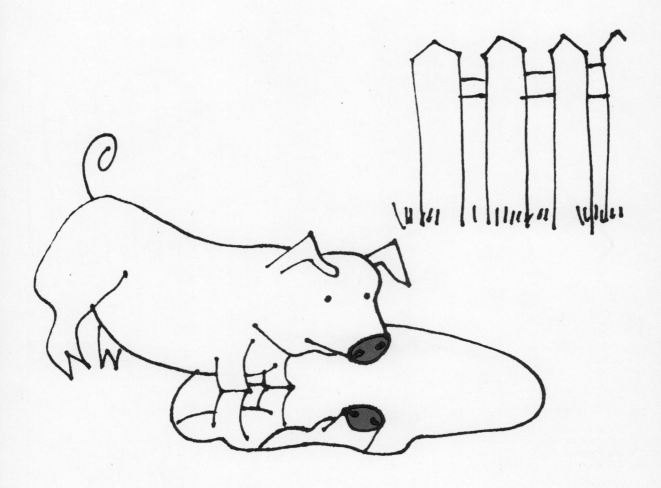

Jig is a big pig.

Jig can dig and dig.

Mag can dig and dig.

Did Jig win? Did Mag win?

Jig did win.

Jig and Mag ran.

Mag can tag Jig.

Mag did win.